Pressing
RESET
— for —
Brazilian
Jiu-Jitsu

original strength

Original strength

Pressing RESET for Brazilian Jiu-Jitsu
by Original Strength

Published by OS Press - Fuquay-Varina, NC

Contributor:

Doug Wright - themovementprof@gmail.com

ISBN:
Paperback: 978-1-64184-395-9

Thank you to JETLAUNCH.net for editing and book design.

Medical Disclaimer

You must get your physician's approval before beginning this program. These recommendations are not medical guidelines but are for educational purposes only. You must consult your physician prior to starting this program or if you have any medical condition or injury that is contraindicated to performing physical activity.

See your physician before starting any exercise or nutrition program. If you are taking any medications, you must talk to your physician before starting any exercise program. If you experience any lightheadedness, dizziness, or shortness of breath while exercising, stop the movement and consult a physician.

It is strongly recommended that you have a complete physical examination if you live a sedentary lifestyle,have high cholesterol, high blood pressure, diabetes, are overweight, or if you are over thirty years old. Please discuss all nutritional changes with your physician or a registered dietician. Please follow your Doctor's orders.

All forms of exercise pose some inherent risks. The contributors, authors, editors, and publishers advise readers to take full responsibility for their own safety and know their limits. When using the exercises in this program, do not move into pain.

Pressing
RESET

ORIGINAL STRENGTH
for Brazilian Jiu-Jitsu

Brazilian Jiu-Jitsu (BJJ) is based on the principles of *leverage* and *efficiency*. Whether you practice this martial art for self-defense, competition, exercise, or just for fun, *efficient* use of energy and movement can significantly impact performance and enjoyment. What if there was a simple way to *leverage* your natural human design to enhance your BJJ experience as well as your overall quality of life?

This booklet is not meant to be an instruction manual on how to practice Brazilian Jiu-Jitsu. What it does offer is a window into a movement philosophy that contains building blocks for your BJJ foundation. This approach, known as Original Strength, provides a template for any individual to restore or upgrade their movement potential and skill level.

The goal of Original Strength is to help people realize a level of strength and control that removes limitations. This state is referred to as reflexive strength. It is the body's ability to anticipate, prepare, and respond to movement before and as it happens. Is there a more ideal place than the BJJ mat to use and explore the beauty of reflexive strength?

Let's roll on.

Pressing RESET for Brazilian Jiu-Jitsu

Original Strength is based on the Three Pillars of Human Movement:

1. Breathe with the diaphragm (i.e. belly breathing).
2. Activate the Vestibular System (i.e. balance and sensory integration system).
3. Engage in contralateral patterns or midline crossing movements (i.e. crawling, walking).

The Three Pillars speak directly to foundational elements of BJJ. First, we must breathe *efficiently* to manage our energy and our mindset. Second, the Vestibular System communicates with the brain to provide information that harmonizes movement and balance. Third, just like crawling and walking coordinate the use of opposite arms and legs, we use contralateral patterns in BJJ.

In order to *tap* into the benefits of the Three Pillars, we need methods to hone our craft. Just as drilling techniques and positions can refine our BJJ skills to eliminate wasted effort and optimize execution, we can sharpen our mind-body connection using an approach called Pressing RESET. This approach consists of refreshing and stimulating the central nervous system through five fundamental movement patterns:

1. Diaphragmic/Belly Breathing
2. Head Control
3. Rolling
4. Rocking
5. Crawling

The following pages provide an introduction and *belt system* to familiarize the reader with each type of RESET. Like BJJ, everyone starts to "develop their own game" as they practice Pressing RESET. The more you progress, however, the more likely it is you will understand and appreciate the simple and effective nature of Original Strength.

△ Look for the TRIANGLE symbol as you review the RESETS. It contains bonus information regarding the RESET or offers additional insight on the connection between Original Strength and Brazilian Jiu-Jitsu.

Pressing
RESET

Breathe with the Diaphragm

WHITE BELT CONCEPT: THE FOUNDATION

Why?

- As in life, the foundation of Brazilian Jiu-Jitsu is breathing.
- Diaphragmatic breathing calms your nervous system.
- A calm mind relaxes the body. Relaxation heightens focus, self-awareness, sensitivity, and response.
  △ Without *efficient* breathing, a BJJ practitioner cannot manage energy. Movement, technique, and execution will suffer.
  △ With proper and *efficient* breathing, you can unlock your BJJ potential.

Tap into the power of your diaphragm so you don't *tap out* on the mat!

---

*TONGUE PLACEMENT: As you perform the RESETS, always keep the tongue connected to the roof of your mouth with your lips closed. Think of the tongue as an antenna. Beyond facilitating proper breathing with the diaphragm, positioning the antenna correctly will give your nervous system the best reception possible from the information it receives. Better input to the nervous system results in better movement output.

Position #1

CONSTRUCTIVE REST POSITION

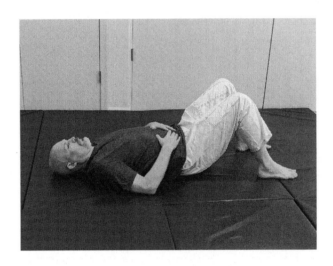

- Lie on your back with your feet flat on the floor and knees pointed toward the ceiling.
- Tongue connected to the roof of your mouth.
- Inhale through your nose and feel your belly, lower back, and sides expand like you are filling a balloon.
- Exhale slowly through the nose until the balloon is completely empty.
   - △ It is okay to feel the air roll up into and be released from your ribcage as you inhale and exhale, but your shoulders should not shrug toward your ears while you breathe.

Position #2

CONSTRUCTIVE REST POSITION

(BUTTERFLY GUARD VARIATION)

- Start on your back in a Constructive Rest Position, then connect the soles of your feet and let your legs relax towards the sides of the room.
- Tongue connected to the roof of your mouth.
- Inhale through your nose and feel your belly, lower back, and sides expand like you are filling a balloon.
- Exhale slowly through the nose until the balloon is completely empty.
  - △ Let your legs relax further toward the floor with each inhale/exhale cycle.

RESET #2

Head Control

BLUE BELT CONCEPT: THE VESTIBULAR SYSTEM

Why?

- The Vestibular System, your balance system, resides in the head. This system is also tied to every muscle in the body.

- The eyes lead the head and the head leads the body.

- Head control influences balance, posture, and coordination.

- Practicing head control nourishes the Vestibular System and creates a foundation for strength.

  △ In BJJ, if someone controls your head, they can control your posture and movement. *Example: Shoulder of Justice.*

  △ Head control impacts your level of execution. *Example: Upa Mount Escape.*

Movement #1

HEAD NODS FROM BASE

- Start on your hands and knees.
- Tongue connected to the roof of your mouth.
- Look down at your chest like you are checking the knot of your BJJ belt, then look up to the ceiling.
- △ Alternative: Perform head nods side to side by looking over each shoulder.
- △ Head nods are a great way to loosen up your neck for BJJ training.

Movement #2

CHIN TUCK

- Lie on your back and gently pull your knees toward your chest.

- Make sure your tailbone is off the floor.

- Tongue connected to the roof of your mouth.

- Tuck the chin and roll your head toward your chest.

- The eyes should lead the head as it is rolling up/ forward.

- Raise and lower the head in a slow/controlled manner or hold the head in the tucked position for several seconds.

  △ Holding the head in a tucked position will add "load" to the diaphragm to develop strength.

Movement #3

CHIN TUCK

(CROSS COLLAR GRIP VARIATION)

- Lie on your back and gently pull your knees toward your chest.
- Cross your feet and make sure your tailbone is off the floor.
- Raise your arms towards the ceiling then connect them like a *cross collar choke.*
- Tongue connected to the roof of your mouth.
- Tuck the chin and roll your head toward your chest.
- The eyes should lead the head as it is rolling up/forward.
- Hold the head in the tucked position for several seconds.
  - △ Practicing this position will "load" the core as you simulate the *closed guard*.

RESET #3

Rolling

PURPLE BELT CONCEPT: ROTATIONAL STRENGTH
AND STABILITY

Why?

- Rolling connects the shoulders and hips.

- It nourishes the spine and builds strength and stability through the torso (the "X").

- Rolling allows your brain and body to absorb and process input from the ground.

  △ In BJJ, we constantly twist, turn, and rotate to establish and hold positions.

  △ Learning how to integrate the "X" will allow you to move with more fluidity and integrity on the mat.

Movement #1

LOWER BODY ROLLING

- Lie on your back with your arms and legs extended.
- Bring your knee across your body (like you are creating a *knee shield* or preparing a frame for a *scissor sweep)*.
- Continue moving the leg as your body turns through the hips and torso to take you to your belly.
- From your belly, reverse the movement by bending the leg and stepping back across your centerline.
- Keep the upper half of your body relaxed as you gently spiral to your back.

  Δ A gentle way to establish mobile hips and move more effortlessly for BJJ.

Movement #2

ELEVATED ROLL

- Start in a plank/push-up position.
- Use your right leg to step back across your body.
- As you step, your right hand will leave the ground and begin to follow the turn of the body.
- Your right foot plants on the ground as your right hand reaches toward the sky.
- To reverse, reach your right arm towards the ground and your lower body will follow to return to the plank/push-up position.

Movement #3

ELEVATED ROLL

(KIMURA / HIP BUMP VARIATION)

• Perform the Elevated Roll.

• From the arm-to-sky position, rotate the arm and move it down behind your back.

• Instead of returning straight to the starting plank/push-up position, allow your arm to "thread the needle" between your body and the floor.

• Continue alternating between the two positions in a fluid manner.

△ Notice how the arm resembles a *kimura* while it is behind the back, then the motion transfers to "clearing a post" on a *hip bump sweep*.

△ A modification for this exercise is demonstrated in Movement #4.

Movement #4

MODIFIED KIMURA / HIP BUMP ROLL

- Begin with one knee on the ground and the other leg extended.

- Perform your *kimura* and *hip bump* arm movements from this alignment.

- Allow your spine and torso to naturally follow your arm motions.

RESET #4

Rocking

BROWN BELT CONCEPT: INTEGRATION

Why?

- Integrates the body physically and neurologically.
- Coordinates the joints from head to toe.
- Gentle strength training.
- Restores posture.
  - △ Develops your understanding of *base* and *weight distribution*.

Movement #1

QUADRUPED ROCKING

- Start on your hands and knees.
- Tongue connected to the roof of your mouth.
- Keep your head up and look at the horizon.
- Rock towards your hands then back towards your feet.
- Keep the natural curves in your back. Do not let the lower back round.
    - △ Experiment with different foot and hand positions.
    - △ This is a great way to warm up your body and calibrate your nervous system prior to training.

Movement #2

QUADRUPED ROCKING

(WINDSHIELD WIPER VARIATION)

- Start on your hands and knees.
- Tongue connected to the roof of your mouth.
- Keep your head up and look at the horizon.
- As you rock forward, *windshield wiper* both legs to one side and rock back.
- When you rock forward again, *windshield wiper* both legs to the opposite side.

△ A great way to learn and practice the *windshield wiper* movement for *guard passing*.

Movement #3

CIRCULAR ROCKING

- Start on your hands and knees.
- Tongue connected to the roof of your mouth.
- Keep your head up and look at the horizon.
- Rock in a circular motion.
- Shoulders and hips should move in a coordinated fashion as you circle.

  △ This is a great way to warm up your body and calibrate your nervous system prior to training.

Movement #4

ADDUCTOR ROCKING

- Start from the Quadruped position.

- Extend one leg out to the side with the toes pointed forward.

- Keep your head up and rock back and forth.

  △ Experiment with different hand positions or rock in small circles.

  △ Wake up your adductors and improve your ability to utilize the *closed guard*.

Movement #5

ADDUCTOR ROCKING

(KNEE-ON-BELLY VARIATION)

- Set your body up in standard Adductor Rocking position.

- Using the posted knee, *windshield wiper* your lower leg toward the fully extended leg to establish your *base*.

- Rock back and forth.

  △ Experience a different type of feedback from this *knee-on-belly* leg position.

Movement #6

LEGO ROCKING

- Sit with one shin on the floor, opposite leg posted with knee pointed toward the ceiling.

- Hands up in "ready" position.

- Post your hands on the floor and rock forward in a smooth and controlled manner, then return to the starting position.

- Feel how the hips, knees, ankles, and toes mobilize differently on each leg.

  △ Assists with maintaining *base* and pinning your opponent's limbs with your shins.

RESET #5

Crawling

BLACK BELT CONCEPT: STRENGTH AND CONTROL

Why?

- In Original Strength, crawling essentially refers to coordinating movement between opposite arms and legs.

- Crawling is the template for how we walk and run.

- Crawling is upper-level training for the nervous system, reflexive strength, and control.

  △ Just like tying your BJJ belt to secure your *gi*, crawling ties everything together.

Movement #1

CROSS-CRAWLS

(GROUND VARIATION)

- Lie on your back with arms and legs extended.
- Touch hand or forearm to the opposite leg.

Movement #2

BASELINE CRAWLING

- Start on your hands and knees.

- Tongue connected to the roof of your mouth.

- Keep your head up and look at the horizon.

- Keep your butt down.

- Opposite limbs will move at the same time. For example, as the right arm moves so will the left leg.

- Crawl forward and/or backward.

  △ To increase strength and your understanding of *weight distribution*, crawl at a slower speed or take your knees off the ground.

Movement #3

BIRD DOG

- Start with your hands and knees on the floor.
- Extend one arm and the opposite leg in a "north/south" direction.
- Tongue connected to the roof of your mouth.
- Keep your head up and look at the horizon.
- Flex your spine to touch the extended limbs together. Hand/forearm/elbow to knee.
- As you connect the opposite limbs, allow your eyes and head to lead the movement.
- The cross-lateral action of the limbs allows this to be considered a "crawling" movement.

Movement #4

BIRD DOG COMPASS

- Start in standard Bird Dog with opposite arm and leg extended "north/south".

- Tap opposite limbs together then extend the arm "diagonally" to 45° while returning the leg to its original position.

- Tap opposite limbs again and extend them in an "east/west" direction.

  △ Develops strength and stability through different planes of movement required for BJJ.

Pressing RESET – Training for Life

Experiment with RESETS before training sessions, after training, or even in between drilling your favorite techniques. Here are a few suggestions to get you started:

Daily RESET

- △ BREATHING: Constructive Rest Position x 1 minute.
- △ HEAD CONTROL: Head Nods From Base x 20 repetitions.
- △ ROLLING: Lower Body Roll x 1 minute.
- △ ROCKING: Quadruped Rocking x 1 minute.
- △ CRAWLING: Grounded Cross-Crawls x 1 minute.

BJJ RESET #1: Warm-Up

- △ BREATHING: Constructive Rest Position or Butterfly Guard Variation x 2 minutes.
- △ HEAD CONTROL: Head Nods From Base x 20 repetitions.
- △ HEAD CONTROL: Choose a Chin Tuck position. Hold for 10 seconds x 3 repetitions.
- △ ROLLING: Lower Body Roll x 3 repetitions per side.

- △ ROLLING: Choose an Elevated Roll movement x 1 to 3 repetitions per side.

- △ ROCKING: Choose 3 rocking movements and perform 5 to 10 repetitions of each.

- △ CRAWLING: Grounded Cross-Crawls or Baseline Crawling x 1 minute.

- △ CRAWLING: Bird Dog x 30 seconds or Bird Dog Compass x 10 seconds each position.

BJJ RESET #2: Cool Down

- △ BREATHING: Constructive Rest Position or Butterfly Guard Variation x 2 minutes.

- △ HEAD CONTROL: Head Nods From Base x 20 repetitions.

- △ ROLLING: Lower Body Roll x 3 repetitions per side.

- △ ROCKING: Circular Rocking x 5 repetitions in each direction.

- △ ROCKING: Adductor Rocking x 5 repetitions on each side.

- △ CRAWLING: Grounded Cross-Crawls x 1 minute.

Your
DESIGN

The Power in Your Design

Original Strength is focused on using the power of your natural design to reach your maximum potential on the training mat and in life. The more we Press RESET, the more we strengthen the mind-body connection. In turn, the stronger the connection, the more we embrace it. This process is analogous to our BJJ journey. The more we practice and learn the art, the more we want to practice and learn. It is a true revelation when we enter this frame of mind and our capacity for growth is infinite.

The beauty of the Original Strength philosophy is that you make it your own. You can choose to practice Pressing RESET anytime, anywhere, and in any manner that is most beneficial for you. The result is the removal of limitations that lead you further along the path to the destination of reflexive strength. At that point, anything is possible.

Want to Learn More?

Original Strength is an education company that teaches about the power of human movement and how it can change the world.

This booklet was designed to give you a brief overview of some of the RESETS we do in Original Strength and apply them to your Brazilian Jiu-Jitsu training. Along the way, you may begin to notice that you feel and move better in general. Feel free to feel good as much as you'd like!

We put this together because we know Pressing RESET can help everyone and anyone. If you do nothing more than what is in this booklet, you will notice many changes in how your body moves and feels. It will benefit both your mind and body.

At Original Strength, we teach health, fitness, and education professionals how to get more out of their patients, clients, athletes, and students. The Original Strength System will reestablish a foundation of movement that will make any physical goal easier and more attainable and help improve mental acuity. We do this by conducting clinics, courses, and training designed for professionals in the fitness, health, wellness, sports conditioning, and vestibular and neuromuscular functionality sectors.

If you want to know more about Pressing RESET and regaining your original strength, visit www.originalstrength.net. There you will find a variety of books, free video tutorials (Movement Snax), and a complete listing of our courses, clinics, and OS Certified Professionals near you.

You may want to consider finding an OS Certified Professional. These professionals can conduct an Original Strength Screen and Assessment (OSSA), which is the quickest and easiest way to identify areas your movement system needs to go from good to best. The OSSA allows your OS Professional to pinpoint the best place for you to start Pressing RESET and restoring your original strength.

If you want to feel good and live life better and stronger, find an OS Certified Professional near you.

Press RESET now and live life better because you were awesomely and wonderfully made to accomplish amazing things.

For more information:

Original Strength Systems, LLC
OriginalStrength.net

PressingRESETfor@Originalstrength.net

Printed in Great Britain
by Amazon